Monkey Madness

Written by Rozanne Lanczak Williams
Created by Sue Lewis
Illustrated by Patty Briles

Creative Teaching Press

Monkey Made a Mess

© 2002 Creative Teaching Press, Inc.
Written by Rozanne Lanczak Williams
Illustrated by Patty Briles
Project Manager: Sue Lewis
Project Director: Carolea Williams

Published in the United States of America by:
Creative Teaching Press, Inc.
P.O. Box 2723
Huntington Beach, CA 92647-0723

ISBN: 1-57471-859-2
CTP 3224

Monkey made a mess
with mud.

Monkey made a mess
with mustard.

Monkey made a mess
with milk.

Monkey made a mess
with macaroni.

Monkey made a mess
with the mail.

Is Mom mad?

No, Monkey cleaned up
the mess.

Mom is not mad!

Create your own mess!

I mean book! Finger-paint a "mess" on page one. Use real mud, chocolate pudding, or brown paint. Use mustard or yellow paint on page two, and use white paint on black paper on page three. Glue torn junk-mail envelopes on the next page. Glue macaroni to the last page. Add text to the pages of your messy book.

Laura's Messy Book

Laura made a mess with mud.

Words in *Monkey Made a Mess*

Initial Consonant: *m*	High-Frequency Words	Other
Monkey	a	cleaned
made	with	
mess	is	
mud	no	
mustard	up	
milk	the	
macaroni	not	
mail		
Mom		
mad		